Shoots of Green

Shoots

of Green

Poems for Young Gardeners

Selected by

ELLA BRAMBLETT

Illustrated by Ingrid Fetz

THOMAS Y. CROWELL COMPANY   NEW YORK

MANUFACTURED IN THE UNITED STATES OF AMERICA
L.C. Card 68-11057
2 3 4 5 6 7 8 9 10

ACKNOWLEDGMENTS

For permission to reprint the copyrighted poems in this anthology, acknowledgment is gratefully made to the following:

ABELARD-SCHUMAN LIMITED for "Fall" from *Runny Days, Sunny Days* by Aileen Fisher, © 1958 by Aileen Fisher. All rights reserved.

ABINGDON PRESS for "Thanksgiving" and "Three Dont's" from *Cherry Stones! Garden Swings!* by Ivy O. Eastwick, copyright © 1962 by Abingdon Press; "Berries" and "Ladybird, Ladybird" from *I Rode the Black Horse Far Away* by Ivy O. Eastwick, copyright © 1960 by Abingdon Press.

MRS. BARBARA BAKER for "A Spike of Green" by Barbara Baker.

MARCHETTE CHUTE for "Early Spring" and "Spring Planting" from the book *Rhymes About Ourselves* by Marchette Chute. Copyright 1941 by Marchette Chute.

COLLINS-KNOWLTON-WING, INC., for "The Pumpkin" by Robert Graves.

MRS. H. M. DAVIES, JONATHAN CAPE LIMITED, and WESLEYAN UNIVERSITY PRESS for "The Rain" from *The Complete Poems of W. H. Davies*, copyright © 1963 by Jonathan Cape Limited.

THE LITERARY TRUSTEES OF WALTER DE LA MARE and THE SOCIETY OF AUTHORS as their representative for "Bread and Cherries," "Seeds," and "There Was an Old Woman" by Walter de la Mare.

DENVER WOMAN'S PRESS CLUB for "September" and "Wise Johnny" by Edwina Fallis.

DOUBLEDAY & COMPANY, INC., for "Blue Flowers," "The Florist Shop," "The Flower-Cart Man," "Pushcart Row," and "Vegetables" from *Taxis and Toadstools* by Rachel Field, copyright 1926 by Doubleday & Company, Inc.; "October" from *Gay Go Up* by Rose Fyleman, copyright 1929, 1930 by Doubleday & Company, Inc., with the permission also of THE SOCIETY OF AUTHORS as the literary representative of the estate of the late Rose Fyleman.

E. P. DUTTON & CO., INC., for "Spring," copyright 1941 by Marchette Chute, from the book *Around and About* by Marchette Chute, published 1957 by E. P. Dutton & Co., Inc.; "Garden Song" from the book *Gaily the Troubadour* by Arthur Guiterman, copyright 1936 by E. P. Dutton & Co., Inc., renewal © 1964 by Mrs. Vida Lindo Guiterman; "Fireworks" from the book *The Blackbird in the Lilac* by James Reeves, published 1959 by E. P. Dutton & Co., Inc., with the permission also of JAMES REEVES and OXFORD UNIVERSITY PRESS; "The Snail" by James Reeves from the book *The Wandering Moon* by James Reeves, published 1960 by E. P. Dutton & Co., Inc., with the permission also of JAMES REEVES and WILLIAM HEINEMANN LTD; "Soliloquy of a Tortoise" from the book *The Flattered Flying Fish and Other Poems* by E. V. Rieu, copyright © 1962 by E. V. Rieu, with the permission also of E. V. RIEU and METHUEN & CO., LTD.

GOLDEN PRESS, INC., for "Things of Summer" from *The New Golden Almanac* by Kathryn Jackson. Copyright © 1952 by Golden Press, Inc.

NORENA CARR GRACE, EXECUTRIX OF THE ESTATE OF FRANCES FROST, for "Winter Feast" by Frances Frost.

HARCOURT, BRACE & WORLD, INC., for "Flowers" and "Lesson" from *Windy Morning* by Harry Behn, copyright 1953 by Harry Behn; "A Spark in the Sun" from *Cricket Songs: Japanese Haiku,* translated and © 1964 by Harry Behn; "Waiting" from *The Little Hill* by Harry Behn, copyright 1949 by Harry Behn; "Tomato Time" from *The Moon and a Star* by Myra Cohn Livingston, © 1965 by Myra Cohn Livingston; "My Grasshopper" and "May Day" from *Wide Awake and Other Poems* by Myra Cohn Livingston, © 1959 by Myra Cohn Livingston; "I Don't Know Why" and "I Found" from *Whispers and Other Poems* by Myra Cohn Livingston, © 1958 by Myra Cohn Livingston; "For All the Joys of Harvest" from *Bless This Day* by Elfrida Vipont, © 1958, by Harcourt, Brace & World, Inc., © William Collins Sons & Co Ltd 1958, with the permission also of WILLIAM COLLINS SONS & CO LTD.

HARPER & ROW, PUBLISHERS, for "Tommy" from *Bronzeville Boys and Girls* by Gwendolyn Brooks,copyright © 1956 by Gwendolyn Brooks Blakely; "The Seasons" and "The Snake" from *In the Middle of the Trees* by Karla Kuskin, copyright © 1958 by Karla Kuskin; "Little Seeds We Sow in Spring" from *The Winds That Come from Far Away* by Else Holmelund Minarik, copyright © 1964 by Else Holmelund Minarik; "Grandmother's Garden" from *A World to Know* by James S. Tippett, copyright 1933 Harper & Brothers; "The Little Maple" from *All That Sunlight* by Charlotte Zolotow, copyright © 1967 by Charlotte Zolotow.

HOLT, RINEHART AND WINSTON, INC., for "Blue-Butterfly Day," "Gathering Leaves," and "Lodged" from *Complete Poems of Robert Frost.* Copyright 1923, 1928 by Holt, Rinehart and Winston, Inc. Copyright 1951, © 1956 by Robert Frost.

HOUGHTON MIFFLIN COMPANY for "Marjorie's Almanac" by Thomas Bailey Aldrich.

MRS. FRIEDE ORLEANS JOFFE for "Any Bird" from Father Gander by Ilo Orleans; "The Mole" from *The Zoo That Grew,* by Ilo Orleans, published by Henry Z. Walck, Inc.

MAY JUSTUS for "A Garden Path" by May Justus.

ALFRED A. KNOPF, INC., for "The Snail" from *Flying Fish* by Grace Hazard Conkling, copyright 1926 by Alfred A. Knopf, Inc.; for "Snail," copyright 1947 by Langston Hughes, reprinted from *Selected Poems of Langston Hughes.*

J. B. LIPPINCOTT COMPANY for "Dandelion" from *Poems by a Little Girl* by Hilda Conkling, copyright 1920, 1948 by Hilda Conkling, published by J. B. Lippincott Company; "V Is for Vendor" from *All Around the Town* by Phyllis McGinley, copyright, 1948, by Phyllis McGinley, published by J. B. Lippincott Company.

THE MACMILLAN COMPANY for "The Little Rose Tree" from *Branches Green* by Rachel Field, copyright 1934 by The Macmillan Company, renewed 1962 by Arthur S. Pederson; "The Thorn Trees" from *Branches Green* by Rachel Field, copyright 1924, 1930 by The Macmillan Company; "Brown and Furry," "The City Mouse Lives in a House," "Hurt No Living Thing," "The Lily Has an Air," and "What Is Pink?" from *Sing-Song* by Christina Rossetti, copyright 1924 by The Macmillan Company.

HAROLD OBER ASSOCIATES INCORPORATED for "B Is for Beanseed" and "Peep Primrose" from *The Children's Bells* by Eleanor Farjeon, copyright © 1960 by Eleanor Farjeon, published by Henry Z. Walck, Inc.; "Earth and Sky," copyright 1927, 1955, by Eleanor Farjeon, "The Flower-Seller" and "Vegetables," copyright 1951 by Eleanor Farjeon, "To Any Garden" and "Window-Boxes," copyright 1933, 1961 by Eleanor Farjeon, from *Poems for Children* by Eleanor Farjeon, published by J. B. Lippincott Company, with the permission also of J. B. LIPPINCOTT COMPANY.

G. P. PUTNAM'S SONS for "Names" from *Hop, Skip and Jump* by Dorothy Aldis, copyright 1939 by Dorothy Aldis; "Winter Flower Store" from *Before Things Happen* by Dorothy Aldis, copyright 1934 by Dorothy Aldis.

RANDOM HOUSE, INC., for "Nasturtium" from *A Handful of Flowers* by Mary Britton Miller. © Copyright 1959 by Pantheon Books, Inc.

WILLIAM R. SCOTT, INC., publisher, for "How Do You Know It's Spring?" from *Nibble, Nibble* by Margaret Wise Brown. Copyright 1959 by Roberta B. Rauch.

CHARLES SCRIBNER'S SONS for "Flowers at Night" from *In the Woods, in the Meadow, in the Sky* by Aileen Fisher. Copyright © 1965 by Aileen Fisher.

THE STATE NATIONAL BANK OF CONNECTICUT, AGENT FOR JAMES WELLES SHEARER, for "Fairy Thief" from *Skipping Along Alone* by Winifred Welles, published by The Macmillan Company.

DOROTHY BROWN THOMPSON for "Arbor Day" by Dorothy Brown Thompson.

NANCY BYRD TURNER for "Old Quin Queeribus" by Nancy Byrd Turner.

LOUIS UNTERMEYER for "Corn" by Esther Antin, which first appeared in the anthology *Rainbow in the Sky* edited by Louis Untermeyer, published by Harcourt, Brace & Company, 1935.

THE VIKING PRESS, INC., for "The Butterbean Tent," "Little Rain," "The Rabbit," and "The Worm" from *Under the Tree* by Elizabeth Madox Roberts. Copyright 1922 by B. W. Huebsch, Inc., 1950 by Ivor S. Roberts.

MABEL WATTS for "Maytime Magic" by Mabel Watts.

Contents

Shoots of Green

Spring Is Coming

SPRING SONG

Spring is coming, spring is coming,
   Birdies, build your nest;
Weave together straw and feather,
   Doing each your best.

Spring is coming, spring is coming,
   Flowers are coming too;
Pansies, lilies, daffodillies
   Now are coming through.

Spring is coming, spring is coming,
   All around is fair,
Shimmer and quiver on the river,
   Joy is everywhere.

—William Blake

BLUE-BUTTERFLY DAY

It is blue-butterfly day here in spring,
And with these sky-flakes down in flurry on flurry
There is more unmixed color on the wing
Than flowers will show for days unless they hurry.

But these are flowers that fly and all but sing:
And now from having ridden out desire
They lie closed over in the wind and cling
Where wheels have freshly sliced the April mire.

—*Robert Frost*

EARLY SPRING

I've looked in all the places
  Where flowers ought to grow.
I've pushed aside the branches
  And searched around below
For crocuses or violets
  Or else a buttercup,—
But not a one is showing.
  They ought to hurry up.

—Marchette Chute

PEEP-PRIMROSE

My plot of earth as yet is bare
Of all the bulbs I planted there,
However busy round their roots,
My trees are innocent of shoots.

But by a sooty little stone
Where crouched a bunch of leaves alone,
This morning I stooped down to see,
And oh! Peep-Primrose looked at me.

—Eleanor Farjeon

THE CROCUS

The golden crocus reaches up
To catch a sunbeam in her cup.

—Walter Crane

DAFFODILS

. . . Daffodils
That come before the swallow dares, and take
The winds of March with beauty.

—*William Shakespeare*

DAFFY-DOWN-DILLY

Daffy-down-dilly has come up to town,
In a yellow petticoat and a green gown.

—*Mother Goose*

WISE JOHNNY

Little Johnny-Jump-Up said,
"It must be spring,
I just saw a ladybug
And heard a robin sing."

—*Edwina Fallis*

To Dig and Delve

MAYTIME MAGIC

A little seed
For me to sow . . .

A little earth
To make it grow . . .
A little hole,
A little pat . . .
A little wish,
And that is that.

A little sun,
A little shower . . .
A little while,
And then—a flower!

—*Mabel Watts*

HOW TO SOW BEANS

One for the mouse, one for the crow,
One to rot, and one to grow.

—*Old Rhyme*

LESSON

To plant a seed and watch it grow
Is something every child should do,

And when it blossoms, how it grew
Is something every child should know,

And when its seeds are ripe to sow,
A child may see the old made new.

To grow and gently grow and grow
Is something people should do too.

—Harry Behn

SEEDS

The seeds I sowed—
For weeks unseen—
Have pushed up pygmy
Shoots of green;
So frail you'd think
The tiniest stone
Would never let
A glimpse be shown.

But no; a pebble
Near them lies,
At least a cherry-stone
In size,
Which that mere sprout
Has heaved away,
To bask in sun
And see the day.

—*Walter de la Mare*

A SPIKE OF GREEN

When I went out
The sun was hot,
It shone upon
My flower pot.

And there I saw
A spike of green
That no one else
Had ever seen—

On other days
The things I see
Are mostly old
Except for me.

But this green spike
So new and small
Had never yet
Been seen at all!

—*Barbara Baker*

TOMMY

I put a seed into the ground
And said, "I'll watch it grow."
I watered it and cared for it
As well as I could know.

One day I walked in my back yard,
And oh, what did I see!
My seed had popped itself right out,
Without consulting me.

—Gwendolyn Brooks

SPRING PLANTING

My garden seeds are coming up
  In the most surprising squiggles.
I planted them extremely straight,
  And then they got the wiggles.

—Marchette Chute

SPRING

The leaves are uncurling,
My seedlings are up.
The sunlight is warmer,
We've got a new pup.
The robins are building,
I've painted my bike,
And we can go barefoot
Whenever
we
like.

—Marchette Chute

How Does Your Garden Grow?

TO ANY GARDEN

Garden, grow,
In clump and row,
Golden trumpet, branch of snow,
Bell of blue and drop of white,
Swelling with your fill of light.

Garden, show your shades of green,
Spires of green, and blades of green,
Crinkled leaves upon whose bed
Little yellow stars are spread.

Garden, grow,
Quick and slow,
Some surprise each morning show;
And lovely as your blue and gold,
Are the surprises you withhold.

—Eleanor Farjeon

LODGED

The rain to the wind said,
"You push and I'll pelt."
They so smote the garden bed
That the flowers actually knelt,
And lay lodged—though not dead.
I know how the flowers felt.

—Robert Frost

A SPARK IN THE SUN

A spark in the sun,
this tiny flower has roots
deep in the cool earth.

—Harry Behn

THE GARDENER

The gardener does not love to talk,
He makes me keep the gravel walk;
And when he puts his tools away,
He locks the door and takes the key.

Away behind the currant row
Where no one else but cook may go,
Far in the plots, I see him dig,
Old and serious, brown and big.

He digs the flowers, green, red, and blue,
Nor wishes to be spoken to.
He digs the flowers and cuts the hay,
And never seems to want to play.

Silly gardener! summer goes,
And winter comes with pinching toes,
When in the garden bare and brown
You must lay your barrow down.

Well now, and while the summer stays,
To profit by these garden days,
O how much wiser you would be
To play at Indian wars with me!

—Robert Louis Stevenson

DANDELION

O little soldier with the golden helmet,
What are you guarding on my lawn?
You with your green gun
And your yellow beard,
Why do you stand so stiff?
There is only the grass to fight!

—Hilda Conkling

NAMES

Larkspur and Hollyhock,
Pink Rose and purple Stock,
Lovely-smelling Mignonette,
Lilies not quite opened yet,
Phlox the favorite of bees,
Bleeding Heart and Peonies—
Just their names are nice to say,
Softly,
On a summer's day.

—Dorothy Aldis

THINGS OF SUMMER

Summer's full of smelling things—
  Mint and mignonette,
And clove pinks and new hay,
  And earth that's warm and wet.

Summer's full of things to hear—
  Sound of birds and bees,
And small feet that scurry,
  And rustlings in the trees.

Summer's full of things to touch—
  Grass and leaves and logs,
Shells and sand and water,
  And slippery fish and frogs.

But some things of summer
  Are only for the eyes—
The bloom of scarlet poppies,
  The wings of butterflies.

—*Kathryn Jackson*

THE LITTLE ROSE TREE

Every rose on the little tree
Is making a different face at me!

Some look surprised when I pass by,
And others droop—but they are shy.

These two whose heads together press
Tell secrets I could never guess.

Some have their heads thrown back to sing,
And all the buds are listening.

I wonder if the gardener knows,
Or if he calls each just a rose?

—*Rachel Field*

WINDOW-BOXES

A window-box of pansies
Is such a happy thing,
A window-box of wallflowers
Is a garden for a king,
A window-box of roses
Makes every one stand still
Who sees a garden growing
On a window-sill.

—Eleanor Farjeon

THE LILY HAS AN AIR

The lily has an air,
  And the snowdrop a grace,
And the sweet pea a way,
  And the heartsease a face,—
Yet there's nothing like the rose
  When she blows.

—Christina Rossetti

A SEPAL, PETAL, AND A THORN

A sepal, petal, and a thorn
Upon a common summer's morn,
A flash of dew, a bee or two,
A breeze
A caper in the trees,—
And I'm a rose!

—Emily Dickinson

WHAT IS PINK?

What is pink? a rose is pink
By the fountain's brink.
What is red? a poppy's red
In its barley bed.
What is blue? the sky is blue
Where the clouds float thro'.
What is white? a swan is white
Sailing in the light.
What is yellow? pears are yellow,
Rich and ripe and mellow.
What is green? the grass is green,
With small flowers between.
What is violet? clouds are violet
In the summer twilight.
What is orange? why, an orange,
Just an orange!

—Christina Rossetti

NASTURTIUM

A flame-like flower
Lovely to touch,
Lovely to smell,
Lovely to look at
And tasty as well.
You'll find in its spur,
If you bite it in two,
A delectable drop
Of delectable dew;
Its pretty cool stem
The color of ice,
If you want to chew it,
Tastes awfully nice;
And if you enjoy
A mouthful of heat,
Its pretty green seed
Is delicious to eat.

—Mary Britton Miller

BLUE FLOWERS

Violets in April,
Forget-me-nots in May,
Larkspur in the month of June
To make your gardens gay!
Blue-eyed grasses in the fields
Of sunny-houred July;
August with her harebell hosts,
Blue as sea and sky,
But just before the frost,
And bluest of them all,
Like fairy banners, gentians spread
Their fringes to the fall.

—*Rachel Field*

from I STOOD TIP-TOE ON A LITTLE HILL

Here are sweet peas, on tiptoe for a flight:
With wings of gentle flush o'er delicate white,
And taper fingers catching at all things,
To bind them all about with tiny rings.

—*John Keats*

FLOWERS AT NIGHT

Some flowers close their petals,
blue and red and bright,
and go to sleep all tucked away
inside themselves at night.

Some flowers leave their petals
like windows open wide
so they can watch the goings-on
of stars and things outside.

—Aileen Fisher

from NIGHT

The sun descending in the west,
The evening star does shine;
The birds are silent in their nest,
And I must seek for mine.
The moon like a flower,
In heaven's high bower,
With silent delight
Sits and smiles on the night.

—William Blake

To Pop into the Pot

V IS FOR VEGETABLES

The country vegetables scorn
To lie about in shops,
They stand upright as they were born
In neatly-patterned crops;

And when you want your dinner you
Don't buy it from a shelf,
You find a lettuce fresh with dew
And pull it for yourself;

You pick an apronful of peas
And shell them on the spot,
You cut a cabbage, if you please,
To pop into the pot.

The folk who their potatoes buy
From sacks before they sup,
Miss half of the potato's joy,
And that's to dig it up.

—Eleanor Farjeon

VEGETABLES

A carrot has a green fringed top;
  A beet is royal red;
And lettuces are curious
  All curled and run to head.

Some beans have strings to tie them on,
  And what is still more queer,
Ripe corn is nothing more or less
  Than one enormous ear!

But when potatoes all have eyes,
  Why is it they should be
Put in the ground and covered up—
  Where it's too dark to see?

—*Rachel Field*

TOMATO TIME

On a summer vine, and low,
The fat tomatoes burst and grow;

A green, a pink, a yellow head
Will soon be warm and shiny red;

And on a morning, hot with sun,
I'll find and pick a ripened one.

Warm juice and seeds beneath the skin—
I'll shut my eyes when I bite in.

—*Myra Cohn Livingston*

GRANDMOTHER'S GARDEN

Grandmother's garden
Has walks of brick,
Bordered with flowers
Crowded thick.

Iris, verbenas,
Zinnias, phlox,
Bachelor buttons,
And tall hollyhocks.

Beds of mint
And saxifrage,
Scented herbs
And savory sage.

Back of the beds
Where the flowers grow
Are vegetables planted
Row on row.

Cabbages, onion,
Carrots, peas,
Beets, and tomatoes—
Plenty of these.

Beans and peppers,
Golden corn;
All growing ripe
On a summer morn.

And close to the gate
Is a pumpkin vine
Which I like best
Because it's mine.

—James S. Tippett

THE PUMPKIN

You may not believe it, for hardly could I:
I was cutting a pumpkin to put in a pie,
And on it was written in letters most plain
'You may hack me in slices, but I'll grow
again.'

I seized it and sliced it and made no mistake
As, with dough rounded over, I put it to bake:
But soon in the garden as I chanced to walk,
Why, there was that pumpkin entire on his
stalk!

—Robert Graves

CORN

In early spring when Samuel plows
  And then begins to sow,
I see the yellow seeds of corn,
  And wish I were a crow.

But when the corn is tall as Sam,
  And harvest time is near,
I'd rather be just what I am
  And eat it off the ear.

—Esther Antin

SOLILOQUY OF A TORTOISE ON REVISITING THE LETTUCE BEDS AFTER AN INTERVAL OF ONE HOUR WHILE SUPPOSED TO BE SLEEPING IN A CLUMP OF BLUE HOLLYHOCKS

One cannot have enough
Of this delicious stuff!

—E. V. Rieu

OLD QUIN QUEERIBUS

Old Quin Queeribus—
  He loved his garden so,
He wouldn't have a rake around,
  A shovel or a hoe.

For each potato's eyes he bought
  Fine spectacles of gold,
And mufflers for the corn to keep
  Its ears from getting cold.

On every head of lettuce green—
  What do you think of that?—
And every head of cabbage, too,
  He tied a garden hat.

Old Quin Queeribus—
  He loved his garden so,
He couldn't eat his growing things,
  He only let them grow!

—*Nancy Byrd Turner*

THERE WAS AN OLD WOMAN

There was an old woman
  who lived at Greenwich
Went out with a candle
  to cut herself spinach.

—Walter de la Mare

HAVE YOU SEEN OLD LOVELL?

Have you seen Old Lovell
With his wooden pick and shovel
  Digging up potatoes in the turnpike road?

Have you seen his wife
With a broad-bladed knife
  Scraping the potatoes in the turnpike road?

Have you seen his daughter
With a pail of dirty water
  Washing the potatoes in the turnpike road?

—Unknown

Fly Away Home

A GARDEN PATH

There is a little garden path
  (I play it is a street),
And you could never guess, I know,
When in it I a-walking go
  How many folks I meet.

There's funny Mr. Hoppy Toad,
  Quite elderly and fat,
Who always winks and hurries by
And will not wait for me, though I
  Should like to have a chat.

And Mrs. Snail, who takes her house
  Wherever she must go;
I longed to get a peep inside,
But as the door's not very wide
  I couldn't quite, you know.

One day a whole procession passed,
  A lovely ant parade.
They went like soldiers marching by,
They seemed so orderly and spry
  And not a bit afraid.

I like the little garden path,
  And so, I'm sure, would you.
If you will go with me some day
I'll show you all along the way,
  And all the people too.

—*May Justus*

HURT NO LIVING THING

Hurt no living thing:
  Ladybird, nor butterfly,
Nor moth with dusty wing,
  Nor cricket chirping cheerily,
Nor grasshopper so light of leap,
  Nor dancing gnat, nor beetle fat,
Nor harmless worms that creep.

—*Christina Rossetti*

BROWN AND FURRY

Brown and furry
Caterpillar in a hurry
Take your walk
To the shady leaf, or stalk,
Or what not,
Which may be the chosen spot.
No toad spy you,
Hovering bird of prey pass by you;
Spin and die,
To live again a butterfly.

—*Christina Rossetti*

THE BUTTERBEAN TENT

All through the garden I went and went,
And I walked in under the butterbean tent.

The poles leaned up like a good tepee
And made a nice little house for me.

I had a hard brown clod for a seat,
And all outside was a cool green street.

A little green worm and a butterfly
And a cricket-like thing that could hop went by.

Hidden away there were flocks and flocks
Of bugs that could go like little clocks.

Such a good day it was when I spent
A long, long while in the butterbean tent.

—Elizabeth Madox Roberts

LITTLE RAIN

When I was making myself a game
Up in the garden, a little rain came.

It fell down in a sort of rush,
And I crawled back under the snowball bush.

I could hear the big drops hit the ground
And see little puddles of dust fly round.

A chicken came till the rain was gone;
He had just a very few feathers on.

He shivered a little under his skin,
And then he shut his eyeballs in.

Even after the rain had begun to hush
It kept on raining up in the bush.

One big flat drop came sliding down,
And a ladybug that was red and brown

Was up on a little stem waiting there,
And I got some rain in my hair.

—Elizabeth Madox Roberts

LADYBIRD, LADYBIRD

Ladybird, Ladybird,
where do you hide?

Under a leaf on its
feathery side;
safe from the lightning—
and safe from the rain—
here I shall stay till
the sun shines again.

—Ivy O. Eastwick

MY GRASSHOPPER

My grasshopper died
near the daisy bed,
fell on his back,
and bumped his head
and kicked his feet into the air,
and someone swept him off somewhere.

—Myra Cohn Livingston

THE SNAIL

At sunset, when the night-dews fall,
Out of the ivy on the wall
With horns outstretched and pointed tail
Comes the grey and noiseless snail.
On ivy stems she clambers down,
Carrying her house of brown.
Safe in the dark, no greedy eye
Can her tender body spy,
While she herself, a hungry thief,
Searches out the freshest leaf.
She travels on as best she can
Like a toppling caravan.

—*James Reeves*

THE SNAIL

The snail is very odd and slow.
He has his mind made up to go
The longest way to anywhere
And will not let you steer him there.

Today I met one in the grass
And hadn't time to watch him pass,
But coming back at sunset, I
Discovered him still traveling by.

The grass-blades grew so thick and tall
I asked him why he climbed them all,
And told him I had sometimes found
The shortest way was going 'round

He was not easy to persuade,
To judge by any sign he made,
And when I lectured him some more
Went in his house and shut the door.

—Grace Hazard Conkling

THE WORM

No, little worm, you need not slip
Into your hole, with such a skip;
Drawing the gravel as you glide
On to your smooth and slimy side.

I'm not a crow, poor worm, not I,
Peeping about your holes to spy,
And fly away with you in air,
To give my young ones each a share.

O no, I'm only looking about,
To see you wriggle in and out,
And drawing together your slimy rings,
Instead of feet, like other things:

So, little worm, don't slide and slip
Into your hole, with such a skip!

—Ann Taylor

THE WORM

Dickie found a broken spade
And said he'd dig himself a well;
And then Charles took a piece of tin,
And I was digging with a shell.

Then Will said he would dig one too.
We shaped them out and made them wide,
And I dug up a piece of clod
That had a little worm inside.

We watched him pucker up himself
And stretch himself to walk away.
He tried to go inside the dirt,
But Dickie made him wait and stay.

His shining skin was soft and wet.
I poked him once to see him squirm.
And then Will said, "I wonder if
He knows that he's a worm."

And then we sat back on our feet
And wondered for a little bit.
And we forgot to dig our wells
A while, and tried to answer it.

And while we tried to find it out,
He puckered in a little wad,
And then he stretched himself again
And went back home inside the clod.

—Elizabeth Madox Roberts

THE WORM

When the earth is turned in spring
The worms are fat as anything.

And birds come flying all around
To eat the worms right off the ground.

They like worms just as much as I
Like bread and milk and apple pie.

And once, when I was very young,
I put a worm right on my tongue.

I didn't like the taste a bit,
And so I didn't swallow it.

But oh, it makes my Mother squirm
Because she *thinks* I ate that worm!

—*Ralph Bergengren*

A BIRD

A bird came down the walk:
He did not know I saw;
He bit an angle-worm in halves
And ate the fellow, raw.

And then he drank a dew
From a convenient grass,
And then hopped sidewise to the wall
To let a beetle pass.

—Emily Dickinson

ANY BIRD

I haven't a palace,
I haven't a throne,
There isn't a thing
In the world I own.

I bathe in the bird-bath,
I perch on the trees;
I come and go
Whenever I please.

But everyone's garden
Is open and free,
There's always a crumb
Or a worm there for me.

I fly where I will,
By woodland or sea;
The whole world is mine;
I'm rich as can be!

—Ilo Orleans

GARDEN SONG

Bee-balm for humming-birds,
Roses for the bee,
Larkspur for butterflies
And hollyhocks for me;
Blue flax for orioles
To mend their hanging nests,
But bee-balm for humming-birds,
Our ever-welcome guests.

—*Arthur Guiterman*

THE RABBIT

When they said the time to hide was mine,
I hid back under a thick grape vine.

And while I was still for the time to pass,
A little gray thing came out of the grass.

He hopped his way through the melon bed
And sat down close by a cabbage head.

He sat down close where I could see,
And his big still eyes looked hard at me,

His big eyes bursting out of the rim,
And I looked back very hard at him.

—*Elizabeth Madox Roberts*

A FRIEND IN THE GARDEN

He is not John the gardener,
And yet the whole day long
Employs himself most usefully
The flower-beds among.

He is not Tom the pussy-cat;
And yet the other day,
With stealthy stride and glistening eye,
He crept upon his prey.

He is not Dash, the dear old dog,
And yet, perhaps, if you
Took pains with him and petted him,
You'd come to love him too.

He's not a blackbird, though he chirps
And though he once was black;
But now he wears a loose, grey coat,
All wrinkled in the back.

He's got a very dirty face,
And very shining eyes!
He sometimes comes and sits indoors;
He looks—and p'raps is—wise.

But in a sunny flower-bed
  He has his fixed abode;
He eats the things that eat my plants—
  He is a friendly TOAD.

—Juliana Horatia Ewing

THE SNAKE

A snake slipped through the thin green grass
A silver snake
I watched it pass
It moved like a ribbon
Silent as snow.
I think it smiled
As it passed my toe.

—Karla Kuskin

THE CITY MOUSE LIVES IN A HOUSE

The city mouse lives in a house;—
  The garden mouse lives in a bower,
He's friendly with the frogs and toads,
  And sees the pretty plants in flower.

The city mouse eats bread and cheese;—
  The garden mouse eats what he can;
We will not grudge him seeds and stalks,
  Poor little timid furry man.

—Christina Rossetti

THE MOLE

Think a moment
  Of the mole,
Who spends a lifetime
  In a hole.

Day or night
  The mole is found
Burrowing
  Beneath the ground.

Poor, blind mole,
  It is a shame—
Your day and night
  Are just the same!

—Ilo Orleans

Come Buy, Come Buy

BREAD AND CHERRIES

"Cherries, ripe cherries!"
  The old woman cried,
In her snowy white apron,
  And basket beside;
And the little boys came,
  Eyes shining, cheeks red,
To buy bags of cherries
  To eat with their bread.

—Walter de la Mare

V IS FOR THE VENDOR

V is for the Vendor
  A very vocal man.
He drives about in summer
  With a vegetable van.
And everybody listens
  To his voice upon the breeze,
Calling "Strawberries, Strawberries!
  Fresh green peas!"

—Phyllis McGinley

THE FLOWER-CART MAN

When it's just past April
  And going on May,
The bent old Flower Man
  Comes our way.

His clothes are very baggy,
  His horse is lean and gray,
But, like a walking garden,
  His cart with plants is gay.

All filled with nodding rose trees
  To make your parlor bright,
With tulips for your table,
  Or daisies gold and white.

With pansy plants and lilies,
  Primrose and daffodil,
And red geraniums in pots
  To trim your window sill.

—*Rachel Field*

PUSHCART ROW

In rain or shine; in heat or snow;
The pushcarts stretch in a long green row,
Close to the curb as they can crowd,
With men all shouting their wares aloud.
If you have need of a lettuce head,
Or a bunch of radishes shiny red,
Of onions, carrots, or cauliflower,
Oranges sweet or lemons sour,
Polished apples or dripping greens,
Fat little mushrooms, thin string beans.
Of fruits and berries plump and round,
By the basket, by the pound—
Bring out your purse and take your pick
Where the two-wheeled pushcarts cluster thick;
Where dogs and children play about
Wheels and pavement and gutter-spout;
Where the women wear shawls and earrings gold,
And the men are mostly brown and old
With selling their wares in shine or snow
On the cobblestones of Pushcart Row.

—Rachel Field

THE FLOWER-SELLER

The Flower-Seller's fat and she wears a big shawl,
She sits on the kerb with her basket and all,
The wares that she sells are not very dear,
And are always the loveliest things of the year.
Daffodils in April,
Purple flags in May,
Sweet peas like butterflies
Upon a summer day,
Brown leaves in autumn,
Green leaves in spring,
And berries in the winter
When the carol-singers sing.
The Flower-Seller sits with her hands in her lap,
When she's not crying Roses she's taking a nap,
Her bonnet is queer, and she calls you My Dear,
And sells you the loveliest things of the year.

—Eleanor Farjeon

THE FLORIST SHOP

Florist shops are beautiful,
All damply green and dimly cool,
And the men who keep them are sure to be
A little baggy about the knee,
With voices pleasant and rather low
From living along with things that grow;
For you can't stay noisy and hurried where
Petal on petal fills the air
With spiciness, and every tree
Is hung with gayest greenery.
Grocers bustle and butchers shout,
Tradesmen tramp noisily in and out,
But florists are quiet men and kind,
With a sort of fragrance of the mind.

—*Rachel Field*

WINTER FLOWER STORE

In winter time our flower store
Is frosted over with the cold.
Through the windows and the door
Comes a blur of rosy gold.
Chrysanthemums? Geraniums? Roses?
Is that a pink azalea tree?
Standing there with tight pressed noses
We can only almost see.

—Dorothy Aldis

TROUBLE IN THE GREENHOUSE

Three big cats in a greenhouse.
Oh! they look so meek,
So sage and sleek,
That but for the clash
And the sudden crash,
And the broken pots
Of forget-me-nots,
And upset roses,
And dingy noses,
And draggled vines,
And tangled twines,
And broken pink,
You'd never think
What a fearful fuss
And hopeless muss
Could be made in a hurry
And velvet flurry
By three meek cats in a greenhouse.

—Mary Mapes Dodge

I Found a Four-Leaf Clover

I DON'T KNOW WHY

I don't know why
the sky is blue
or why the raindrops
splatter through

or why the grass
is wet with dew . . . do you?

I don't know why
the sun is round
or why a seed grows
in the ground

or why the thunder
makes a sound . . . do you?

I don't know why
the clouds are white
or why the moon
shines very bright

or why the air
turns black at night . . . do you?

—*Myra Cohn Livingston*

B IS FOR BEANSEED

A Beanseed, a Beanseed,
A pink speckled Beanseed,
I'll plant a fat Beanseed in my little plot,
I'll plant it at night
And I'll shut my eyes tight
And sleep until daybreak, and then I'll see What?

A Ladder, a Ladder,
An endless green Ladder,
All tangled with tendrils and red-and-white bloom;
I'll climb up as high
As the top of the sky
By the leaves of my Ladder, and then I'll see Whom?

A Lady, a Lady,
A beautiful Lady,
With a ring on her finger, a crown on her hair;
I'll kneel on my knee
When the Lady I see,
And she'll beckon me onwards, and I shall go Where?

A Castle, a Castle,
A turreted Castle,
With knights in gold armour and gay serving-men,
And I'll live in the air
With the Lady so fair,
Till my Beanseed is withered, and that will be When?

A Beanseed, a Beanseed,
A pink speckled Beanseed!
I planted a Beanseed in my little plot.
The Castle is crumbled,
The Lady she tumbled,
And the Cook pulled the Beans off to put in the pot.

—Eleanor Farjeon

THE MAGIC VINE

A fairy seed I planted,
So dry and white and old;
There sprang a vine enchanted
With magic flowers of gold.

I watched it, I tended it,
And truly, by and by
It bore a Jack-o'-lantern
And a great Thanksgiving pie.

—Unknown

I FOUND

I found a four-leaf clover,
I put it in my shoe.
I thought my wishes over
And one of them came true.

—Myra Cohn Livingston

FAIRY THIEF

When I go to bed at night,
  Every candle is in bloom,
Silver petals, clear and bright,
  Glisten all around the room.

In the morning, when I waken,
  Only wicks are left, forlorn,
Every blossom has been taken,
  Every tiny stalk been shorn.

Who has tiptoed up the stair?
  Who has danced so soft away,
With a wreath upon his hair,
  In his hands a bright bouquet?

—Winifred Welles

FIREWORKS

They rise like sudden fiery flowers
  That burst upon the night,
Then fall to earth in burning showers
  Of crimson, blue, and white.

Like buds too wonderful to name,
  Each miracle unfolds,
And catherine-wheels begin to flame
  Like whirling marigolds.

Rockets and Roman candles make
  An orchard of the sky,
Whence magic trees their petals shake
  Upon each gazing eye.

—*James Reeves*

HARVEST

The boughs do shake and the bells
  do ring,
So merrily comes our harvest in,
Our harvest in, our harvest in,
So merrily comes our harvest in.

We've ploughed, we've sowed,
We've reaped, we've mowed,
We've got our harvest in.

—Unknown

FALL

The last of October
we close the garden gate.
(The flowers have all withered
that used to stand straight.)

The last of October
we put the swings away.
The porch looks deserted
where we liked to play.

The last of October
the birds have all flown,
the screens are in the attic,
the sandpile's alone.

Everything is put away
before it starts to snow . . . .
I wonder if the ladybugs
have any place to go?

—*Aileen Fisher*

BERRIES

Red berry,
white berry,
blue berry,
sloe—
Autumn
leaves berries
wherever I
go—
up on the
hills, in the
valley
below
there are
red berry,
white berry,
blue berry,
sloe!

—*Ivy O. Eastwick*

THE THORN TREES

The thorn trees hold their berries high
In crowded scarlet to the sky.
No beads so red were ever seen
When gypsies camp upon a green,
Or such a shine spread to the air
On any patterned luster-ware.
The thorn trees have no need to hide
From pasture, road, or countryside.
Too bright of skin and sharp of core,
Theirs is no fruit for housewife's store.
Thornberries need be only gay
To give the heart a holiday.

—Rachel Field

BABY SEEDS

In a milkweed cradle,
Snug and warm,
Baby seeds are hiding,
Safe from harm.
Open wide the cradle,
Hold it high!
Come Mr. Wind,
Help them fly.

—Unknown

AUTUMN FIRES

In the other gardens
   And all up the vale,
From the autumn bonfires
   See the smoke trail!

Pleasant summer over
   And all the summer flowers,
The red fire blazes,
   The grey smoke towers.

Sing a song of seasons!
   Something bright in all!
Flowers in the summer,
   Fires in the fall!

—Robert Louis Stevenson

OCTOBER

The summer is over,
  The trees are all bare,
There is mist in the garden
  And frost in the air.
The meadows are empty
  And gathered the sheaves—
But isn't it lovely
  Kicking up leaves!

John from the garden
  Has taken the chairs;
It's dark in the evening
  And cold on the stairs.
Winter is coming
  And everyone grieves—
But isn't it lovely
  Kicking up leaves!

—*Rose Fyleman*

GATHERING LEAVES

Spades take up leaves
No better than spoons,
And bags full of leaves
Are light as balloons.

I make a great noise
Of rustling all day
Like rabbit and deer
Running away.

But the mountains I raise
Elude my embrace,
Flowing over my arms
And into my face.

I may load and unload
Again and again
Till I fill the whole shed,
And what have I then?

Next to nothing for weight,
And since they grew duller
From contact with earth,
Next to nothing for color.

Next to nothing for use.
But a crop is a crop,
And who's to say where
The harvest shall stop?

—Robert Frost

A Song of Seasons

LITTLE SEEDS WE SOW IN SPRING

Little seeds we sow in spring
growing while the robins sing,
give us carrots, peas and beans,
tomatoes, pumpkins, squash and greens.

And we pick them,
one and all,
through the summer,
through the fall.

Winter comes, then spring, and then
little seeds we sow again.

—Else Holmelund Minarik

THE YEAR'S ROUND

The crocus, while the days are dark,
  Unfolds its saffron sheen;
At April's touch, the crudest bark
  Discovers gems of green.

Then sleep the seasons, full of might;
  While slowly swells the pod
And rounds the peach, and in the night
  The mushroom bursts the sod.

The Winter falls; the frozen rut
  Is bound with silver bars;
The snow-drift heaps against the hut,
  And night is pierced with stars.

—Coventry Patmore

ARBOR DAY

To plant a tree! How small the twig,
And I beside it—very big.
A few years pass; and now the tree
Looks down on very little me.
A few years more—it is so high
Its branches seem to touch the sky.
I did not know that it would be
So vast a thing to plant a tree.

—Dorothy Brown Thompson

MAY DAY

So soft came the breath
of the lavender Spring
in a basket of lilacs
it made me sing.

—*Myra Cohn Livingston*

MARJORIE'S ALMANAC

Robins in the tree-top,
  Blossoms in the grass,
Green things a-growing
  Everywhere you pass;

Sudden little breezes,
  Showers of silver dew,
Black bough and bent twig
  Budding out anew;

Pine-tree and willow-tree,
  Fringed elm, and larch
Don't you think that Maytime's
  Pleasanter than March?

—*Thomas Bailey Aldrich*

HOW DO YOU KNOW IT'S SPRING?

How do you know it's Spring?
And how do you know it's Fall?
Suppose your eyes were always shut
And you couldn't see at all.
Could you smell and hear the Spring?
And could you feel the Fall?

—*Margaret Wise Brown*

SEPTEMBER

A road like brown ribbon,
A sky that is blue,
A forest of green
With that sky peeping through.

Asters, deep purple,
A grasshopper's call,
Today it is summer,
Tomorrow is fall.

—*Edwina H. Fallis*

THANKSGIVING

Thank You
  for all my hands can hold—
    apples red,
      and melons gold,
        yellow corn
          both ripe and sweet,
            peas and beans
              so good to eat!

Thank You
  for all my eyes can see—
    lovely sunlight,
      field and tree,
        white cloud-boats
          in sea-deep sky,
            soaring bird
              and butterfly.

Thank You
  for all my ears can hear—
    birds' song echoing
      far and near,
        songs of little
          stream, big sea,
            cricket, bullfrog,
              duck and bee!

—Ivy O. Eastwick

FOR ALL THE JOYS OF HARVEST

For all the joys of harvest,
  For all the heavy toil,
For sunshine and for showers,
  And for the fruitful soil;

For wheat and oats and barley,
  And rows of beans and peas,
For food for men and cattle,
  We offer thanks for these.

God bless the harvest workers,
  The farmer and his men,
The ploughing and the sowing
  Till harvest comes again.

—*Elfrida Vipont*

THE SEASONS

The leaves have left without a warning
I noticed when I woke this morning.
The spring arrived and then it went.
The summer came and now it's spent.
The leaves turned yellow, crimson, brown
And drifted, sifted slowly down.
And now the trees look bare and thin
It's time for winter to begin
And make their branches thick with snow
Because that's how the seasons go.

—Karla Kuskin

THE LITTLE MAPLE

Little gray tree
like a skeleton,
how green you were
this summer.
What a rustling rippling sound you made
in the wind.

Little tree
how you flamed!
How you were gay
before you turned
so stiff and gray.

—*Charlotte Zolotow*

WINTER FEAST

Now the small birds come to feast
on mountain ash and winterberry.
They teeter on the leafless twig,
their little throats are pert and merry.

What matter if the earth is lost
beneath the sparkle of the snow?
From crimson barberry to red
rose hips, the gay birds bob and blow,

and whistle to the silver woods,
and chortle to the sun's pale gold,
"As long as scarlet berries grow,
we'll fly like brown leaves through
the cold!"

—*Frances Frost*

EARTH AND SKY

(They talk to each other on Christmas Eve.)

Earth.	Oh Sky, you look so drear!
Sky.	Oh Earth, you look so bare!
Earth.	How chilly you appear!
Sky.	How empty you lie there!
Sky.	My winds blow icy cold.
Earth.	My flowers have gone from me.
Sky.	Yet I've one Star of gold.
Earth.	And I have one green Tree.
Sky.	I'll set my Star on high
	Alone in its own light
	For any Child to spy
	Who wakes on Christmas Night.
Earth.	I'll hang my Tree with toys,
	Like fruit and flowers gay,
	For little girls and boys
	To pick on Christmas Day.
They say	Then let the soft snow fall,
together.	And let the cold wind blow!
	We have in spite of all
	A pretty thing to show;

Yes, Christmas Eve and Morn
We'll show our pretty thing
To every baby born
Of Beggar-man or King.

Earth.	Oh Sky, you look so clear!
Sky.	Oh Earth, you look so fair!
Earth.	How bright your Star shines here.
Sky.	How green your Tree grows there.

—*Eleanor Farjeon*

WAITING

Dreaming of honeycombs to share
With her small cubs, a mother bear
Sleeps in a snug and snowy lair.

Bees in their drowsy, drifted hive
Sip hoarded honey to survive
Until the flowers come alive.

Sleeping beneath the deep snow
Seeds of honeyed flowers know
When it is time to wake and grow.

—*Harry Behn*

Index of Authors

Index of Titles

Index of First Lines

ABOUT THE AUTHOR

Ella Bramblett, a graduate of Middle Tennessee State University in Murfreesboro, received her M.A. from George Peabody College for Teachers in Nashville, Tennessee. She has taken advanced graduate work at the Colorado State College at Greeley. At present she teaches at Towson State College in Baltimore, Maryland. Miss Bramblett makes her home in Towson, Maryland.

ABOUT THE ILLUSTRATOR

Ingrid Fetz's illustrations have appeared in numerous magazines, newspapers, and books. She considers her primary interests to be books and children. While teaching art to children, she was also the Director of the Cambridge Art Center for Children in Cambridge, Massachusetts.

Miss Fetz attended the Cambridge School of Art, and the Workshop of Advertising and Editorial Art and Columbia University in New York. She lives in Ossining, New York.